Marco I

He's a joker
messing ab
always mea
if he someti
things wron

12/24
50p

Philippa Feltpen

A real peacemaker, she
helps keep the other
Pens in order by sorting
out arguments and giving
good advice.

Waxy Max

He's very sporty and
football mad. On the
outside, he's tough,
but underneath he's
got the biggest heart.

What's this
lot going to be
up to inside?

Squiggle and Splodge

The Scribble twins! They're
both quiet, both shy.
Although they may not
look alike, they do almost
everything together.

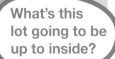

Enter ...

How can I follow Jesus, Splodge?

Let's try and find out inside!

Pens

Helping you to get to know God more

Following JESUS

Written by
Alexa Tewkesbury

Every day a short Bible reading is brought to life with the help of the Pens characters. A related question and prayer apply this to daily life. Written in four sections, two focusing on the lives of Pens and two on Bible characters, young children will be inspired to learn more of God and His Word.

What's inside?

Living with Jesus — Day 1

Always with Us – Stormy weather — Day 11

Living like Jesus — Day 16

One Kind Man – A Samaritan helps out — Day 26

Mixed Sources
Product group from well-managed
forests and other controlled sources
www.fsc.org Cert no. SGS-COC-003963
© 1996 Forest Stewardship Council

Day 1 LIVING WITH JESUS

'All the people were amazed at the mighty power of God.'
(Luke 9 v 43)

The great adventure

It was a brand-new day, with wonderful things to discover and exciting adventures to have.

What shall we do?

We could go to the park.

'We could go shopping,' replied Gloria.

'We could play football,' grinned Max.

'We could play hide and seek,' squealed Squiggle and Splodge.

'What about the beach?' asked Marco.

'Why not ask Jesus?' said Philippa. 'He wants the best for us and, if you ask Him, you never know where He'll take you, or what He'll ask you to do.'

 Life with Jesus is a life full of adventure.

What adventures would you like to have?

Pens Prayer

Lord, open my eyes to see how wonderful Your world is. Open my heart to the excitement of every day with You. Amen.

Day 2 — Living with Jesus

'Run, then, in such a way as to win the prize.'
(1 Corinthians 9 v 24)

Ready, steady, go!

It was sports day in Pens' town. There were running races, hopping races, egg and spoon races and skipping races.

Max, Sharpy and Denzil were doing a running race.

'I'm the fastest,' boasted Max.

'Says who?' retorted Denzil. 'I'm the fastest.'

Ready … steady … GO!

They shot off. Sharpy kept his eyes fixed on the winning post; but Max and Denzil didn't. They were too busy keeping an eye on each other – so busy that they weren't fast enough.

Max and Denzil didn't win the race.

Clever Sharpy did.

 Fixing our eyes on Jesus keeps us close to God.

What different types of races do you have at your school sports day?

Pens Prayer

Dear Lord Jesus, please help me to keep my eyes on You, so that, through You, I can be with God forever. Amen.

Day 3

Living with Jesus

'Anyone who is joined to Christ is a new being; the old is gone, the new has come.' (2 Corinthians 5 v 17)

Brand-new

Squiggle and Splodge live here

When Squiggle and Splodge first moved to Pens' town, everything was new for them. They had a new house and a new garden. They even had a new garden shed. There was a new park to play in and a new school where they could learn new things. There were new shops to go shopping in, new places to explore and new friends to explore them with.

'Do you know what this is like?' Squiggle cried excitedly.

'Yes!' squealed Splodge. 'It's like having a brand-new life.'

 When we choose to live with Jesus, He makes our lives brand-new.

Is anything in your house brand-new?

Pens Prayer

Jesus! How I love to spend my days with You. Amen.

'If anyone wants to come with me, he must forget self … and follow me.' (Matthew 16 v 24)

Hot and bothered

'What's that?' wondered Max.

He listened.

There it was again … and again – a huffing, puffing sound like a huffing, puffing steam train.

It was Sharpy. He'd been lying in the sun and was very, very hot.

'Oh dear, Sharpy,' said Max. 'It's time for your walk but you look a bit too hot. We'll have to go later.'

Marco shook his head. 'We can't. The fish and chip van's coming and we might miss it.'

'I know,' replied Max, 'but today Sharpy's walk is more important.'

 In the same way, putting Jesus first isn't always easy, but it's always best.

What do you like doing in hot weather to cool yourself down?

Pens Prayer

Dear Jesus, please teach me to listen for Your voice and to follow You happily. Amen.

11

Living with Jesus

'… everything is possible for God.' (Mark 10 v 27)

When Denzil woke up,
he was feeling gloomy.

He got up and had breakfast. The gloom didn't go away. He went outside and played on his skateboard. The gloom was still there.

'Bother,' said Denzil again.

The postman came with an envelope. Denzil opened it. It was a card from Charlotte. Inside she'd written: *Hey, Denzil! Thanks for being such a good friend.*

'Wow,' said Denzil. 'I wasn't expecting that.'

Then a big smile spread across his face and, suddenly, the gloom was gone.

With Jesus, the most unexpected things can happen.

Denzil

When one of your friends needs cheering up, how could you surprise them?

Pens Prayer

Thank You, Lord Jesus, for the unexpected ways You show You love me. Amen.

Day 6 — Living with Jesus

'[Jesus] is the key that opens all the hidden treasures of God's wisdom and knowledge.' (Colossians 2 v 3)

Sharpy's **special** day

14

'Sharpy's birthday,' hissed Philippa.

'What shall we do?' wondered Gloria.

Philippa thought. 'What does Sharpy like?'

'Chasing a ball, Max says,' said Gloria.

'Gobbling up dog treats, Max says,' remembered Philippa.

'Playing on the beach, Max says,' continued Gloria.

'So,' said Philippa, 'let's take Sharpy to the beach on his birthday, with a ball and some treats.'

'Brilliant idea,' smiled Gloria, 'and it's thanks to Max. Because we know Max, we know all about Sharpy, too.'

Getting to know Jesus helps us to get to know God.

How well do you know your friends?

Pens Prayer

Dear Jesus, please help me to look forward to spending time with You so that I can learn more and more about my Father God. Amen.

Living with Jesus

'Christ's message in all its richness must live in your hearts.' (Colossians 3 v 16)

Charlotte's lesson

Learn to read!

Charlotte was helping Squiggle and Splodge to learn to read. They knew the letters of the alphabet. Now Charlotte was showing them how to put the letter sounds together to make words.

'When you can read books,' said Charlotte, 'you can share exciting adventures in fantastic places.'

'But supposing I can never understand storybooks?' worried Splodge. 'Supposing I can't read well enough?'

'You will,' laughed Charlotte. 'If you practise what I'm teaching you, you'll get better and better, and you'll soon discover hundreds of amazing stories.'

 Listening to Jesus and taking notice of His words opens up a whole new world.

Do you have a favourite book? What about a favourite Bible story?

Pens Prayer

Thank You so much, dear Lord, for the Bible, which teaches us about You and Your wonderful love for us. Amen.

'Since you have accepted Christ Jesus as Lord, live in union with him.' (Colossians 2 v 6)

It's hotter than hot! Let's go to the beach.

I'll pack a picnic.

Sharpy sat down and watched.

'I'll grab towels and swimsuits,' shouted Marco.

Sharpy lay down by the front door.

'I'll fetch hats and sun cream,' announced Max.

Sharpy slipped away behind the sofa.

When Pens were ready to go, Gloria called, 'Sharpy!'

Sharpy peeped out.

'You look sad,' frowned Marco. 'Did you think we'd go without you?'

'Funny Sharpy,' smiled Max. 'Where we go, you go. You're one of the gang.'

Wherever you are, whatever you're doing, Jesus loves to be involved.

What are you doing this week? Remember to invite Jesus, too.

Pens Prayer

Share my life, Lord Jesus, please. I am so happy to have You near me. Amen.

Living with Jesus

'… Mary … sat down at the feet of the Lord and listened to his teaching.' (Luke 10 v 39)

Too busy Pens

Philippa wanted a chat, so she went visiting.

Hello, Charlotte.

Can't stop to chat. O... to the libra...

'Hello, Marco,' Philippa said.

'Can't stop to chat,' answered Marco. 'Off to go swimming.'

'Hello, Gloria,' Philippa said.

'Can't stop to chat,' bustled Gloria. 'Off to the shops.'

Disappointed, Philippa was about to go home again when suddenly Charlotte, Marco and Gloria came back.

'Sorry, Philippa,' said Charlotte. 'We shouldn't have rushed away. You always have time for us. Now we want to make time for you.'

 It's important to find special time to spend with Jesus.

When you're at home, where can you go to talk and listen quietly to Jesus?

Pens Prayer

Dear Lord Jesus, when my days are busy, please help me remember to make time for quiet moments just with You. Amen.

The Blackboard and You

Flika goes adventuring

Mad Mike the Monkey

Day 10

Living with Jesus

'… be thankful in all circumstances.'
(1 Thessalonians 5 v 18)

The **big** thank you

Pens were so happy to be living with Jesus that they wanted to say a special thank you prayer.

'But we all want to thank Him for different things,' said Marco.

'Then that's what we'll do,' said Philippa.

Pens thought of one 'thank you' each.

Max thanked Jesus for football in the park; Gloria for beautiful hats; Denzil for exciting surprises; Charlotte for songs to sing; Marco for jokes and tricks; Squiggle and Splodge for each other.

'And for living with us every day,' finished Philippa, 'thank You, Jesus.'

Thanking Jesus every day reminds us how much He has given us.

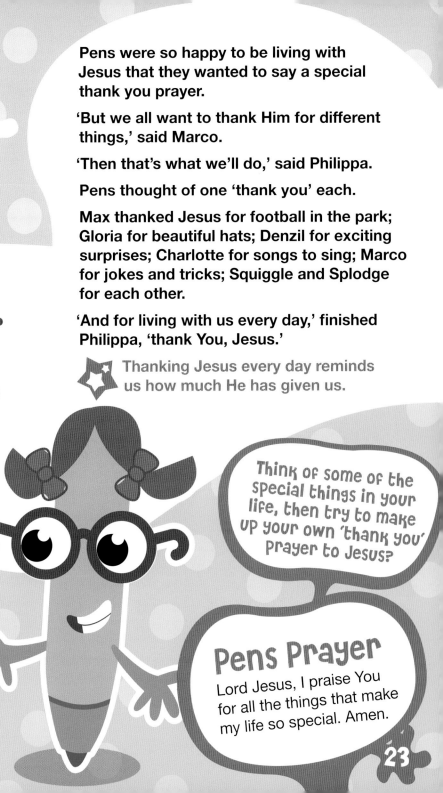

Think of some of the special things in your life, then try to make up your own 'thank you' prayer to Jesus?

Pens Prayer

Lord Jesus, I praise You for all the things that make my life so special. Amen.

ALWAYS WITH US
Stormy weather
Day 11

'… Jesus said to his disciples, "Let us go across to the other side of the lake."' (Mark 4 v 35)

The
boat
ride

Jesus had been busy. Everywhere He went, crowds of people followed Him. They wanted to listen to Him talking about God. If they were ill, they wanted Him to make them better.

At the end of one busy day, Jesus said to His special friends, 'We need a little time off.' So they all climbed into a boat and went sailing across the water.

Jesus was always ready to spend time with people who needed Him.

Who do you enjoy spending time with?

Pens Prayer

Lord Jesus, I want to thank You for being with me every day. Amen.

Always with Us
Stormy weather

Day 12

'Suddenly a strong wind blew up, and the waves began to spill over into the boat ...' (Mark 4 v 37)

Storm!

Out of nowhere, a storm rolled in. 'Oh dear,' Jesus' friends began to think, 'perhaps going sailing isn't a good idea after all.'

The boat swayed from side to side. The boat rocked up and down. Jesus' friends held on tightly but they couldn't stop the water pouring in. When they looked around for Jesus to help them, they saw that He was fast asleep. 'We're going to sink!' they shouted.

Jesus' friends were afraid because they didn't trust Jesus to look after them.

What can you do when you feel afraid?

Pens Prayer

Dear Jesus, thank You for loving me. Please teach me to remember that I can trust in You always. Amen.

Day 13

'Jesus stood up and commanded the wind, "Be quiet!" and he said to the waves, "Be still!" The wind died down, and there was a great calm.' (Mark 4 v 39)

'That's enough'

'Jesus!' His friends shouted at the tops of their voices. 'You need to wake up. We're sinking!'

When Jesus opened His eyes, He wasn't afraid. He just got to His feet and ordered the wind to stop blowing and the waves to stop heaving.

All at once, everything was still.

Jesus took care of His friends.

Have you ever watched a thunderstorm? What appears in the sky?

Pens Prayer

Lord Jesus, You are beside me on sunny days and rainy days, on calm days and stormy days. Thank You. Amen.

Always with Us
Stormy weather

Day 14

'Then Jesus said to his disciples, "Why are you frightened? Have you still no faith?"' (Mark 4 v 40)

Better weather

Jesus' friends could hardly believe their eyes. The storm had listened to Him! Jesus had told it to calm down and it had. The boat had stopped rocking. The water had stopped pouring in. They were safe.

They didn't need to be afraid because Jesus would always take care of them. All He wanted them to do was trust Him.

We can trust Jesus to stay close to us no matter what happens.

What can you wear to help keep you dry in stormy weather?

Pens Prayer

Dear Jesus, please take care of me every day, just as You took care of Your friends in the storm. Amen.

Always with Us
Stormy weather

Day 15

'Who is this man? Even the wind and the waves obey him!' (Mark 4 v 41)

WOW!

Out on the lake, the storm was over and the water was calm again.
The sailing boat carrying Jesus and His friends bobbed gently up and down. Jesus' friends couldn't stop staring at Him. 'Even a storm settles down when He speaks to it,' they thought. 'How powerful He is!'

Jesus is Lord of the whole world!

How many ways can you think of to praise Jesus?

Pens Prayer

Lord of the earth and of the sea and of the sky;
Lord of the air and of the sun and of the moon;
Lord of the wind and of the rain, Lord of us all –
I PRAISE YOU! Amen.

'If you become angry, do not let your anger lead you into sin, and do not stay angry all day.' (Ephesians 4 v 26)

Still friends

Charlotte and Gloria were having a very bad day. They'd had a quarrel which left them both feeling sad

'I hate getting cross,' Charlotte sighed to Denzil.

'I didn't mean anything I said,' Gloria muttered to Philippa.

Denzil suggested to Charlotte, 'Let's go and find Gloria. You can say sorry.'

Philippa smiled at Gloria, 'You need to find Charlotte. You can tell her you're sorry.'

With Denzil and Philippa's help, Charlotte and Gloria found each other. They both said sorry … and shared a HUGE hug.

 If we've been cross with someone, it's important to tell them we're sorry.

Who can you talk to if you feel cross about something?

Pens Prayer

Dear Jesus, sometimes it seems very easy to get angry. Please help me to find it just as easy to say sorry. Amen.

Living like Jesus

'... all of you must ... serve one another ...'
(1 Peter 5 v 5)

The helping hand

36

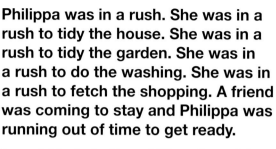

Philippa was in a rush. She was in a rush to tidy the house. She was in a rush to tidy the garden. She was in a rush to do the washing. She was in a rush to fetch the shopping. A friend was coming to stay and Philippa was running out of time to get ready.

'I could help,' offered Max. 'I could do the shopping.'

'*Would* you?' sighed Philippa gratefully. 'I'll make a list.'

'Then, when I get back,' continued Max, 'I can help with everything else.'

 Serving other people means being happy to give our time to help them.

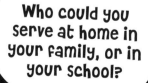 Who could you serve at home in your family, or in your school?

Pens Prayer

Lord Jesus, I want to be like You and to serve people around me. Please help me to be thoughtful every day. Amen.

Day 18 — Living like Jesus

'Leave all your worries with him, because he cares for you.' (1 Peter 5 v 7)

Sleep tight

Squiggle was excited. It was her first night in a new bedroom – all of her own.

Splodge was worried. It was *her* first night in a bedroom without Squiggle – all by herself.

'I don't like this,' she mumbled. 'I don't like being in the dark. I don't like Squiggle not being here. I don't like having no one to talk to.'

'I'm only in the room next door,' said Squiggle kindly. 'Don't be scared. God's with you. You can share all your worries with Him.'

 When Jesus was worried or afraid, He talked to His Father God.

Do you have a special bedtime routine?

Pens Prayer

Father God, thank You for helping me with my worries when I talk to You about them. Amen.

Living like Jesus

'Work hard and do not be lazy.' (Romans 12 v 11)

Lazy Gloria

Hat Couture

Pens had promised to help Charlotte when she moved house. Denzil and Philippa packed. Max and Marco cleaned. Squiggle, Splodge and Sharpy checked the cupboards were empty.

Everyone worked hard.

Everyone except Gloria.

Gloria didn't feel like working. She took a long, bubbly bath. She sipped a long drink of lemonade. She had a long read of a long book. She took so long being lazy that she missed Charlotte's move.

And she missed the special cakes Charlotte had baked to thank all the friends who'd helped her.

 No matter how He was feeling, Jesus worked hard to help people and teach them about God.

What might Charlotte have mixed together to make her cakes?

Pens Prayer

Lord Jesus, if I sometimes feel lazy and unhelpful, may I try to remember You and everything You've done for me. Amen.

Day 20   Living like Jesus

'… be satisfied with what you have.' (Hebrews 13 v 5)

Marco's wishes

Philippa and Marco were out walking. Someone zipped past on a shiny bike.

'Did you see that bike?' cried Marco. 'Brilliant. I wish it was mine.'

Someone whizzed by on a stripy skateboard.

'Did you see that skateboard?' yelled Marco. 'Wow. I wish it was mine.'

Someone scooted past on a snazzy scooter.

'Did you see that scooter?' shouted Marco. 'Cool. I wish it was mine.'

Philippa smiled. 'But, Marco, you've got a bike, and a skateboard, and a scooter. Now stop wishing and enjoy what you have.'

 It's good to thank God for the things we have, rather than wasting time wishing for the things we don't have.

Which are your favourite toys?

Pens Prayer

Dear Jesus, You were born in a stable. You worked as a carpenter. You served God and wanted nothing more. Teach me to be happy with who I am and what I have. Amen.

43

'… your light must shine before people, so that they will see the good things you do and praise your Father in heaven.' (Matthew 5 v 16)

'I can swim!'

It was a big day for Gloria. She'd been trying to learn to swim … for a very long time … and today was the day … SHE DID IT!

Gloria was so excited that she hung balloons on her gate and painted 'I CAN SWIM' on an old bed sheet, which she fixed to her garden fence. Then she put on her best hat and invited all her Pen friends to a tea party to celebrate.

'I'm a swimmer,' she announced proudly, 'and I want everyone to know!'

 Jesus wanted everyone to know God, so everything He did and everything He said showed God to others.

How does God like us to behave with each other?

Pens Prayer

Dear Lord God, when I'm excited, it shows. Please help me to be so excited about being Your friend that other people can see You. Amen.

45

Day 22 — Living like Jesus

'Whoever is faithful in small matters will be faithful in large ones ...' (Luke 16 v 10)

The lost purse

Pen

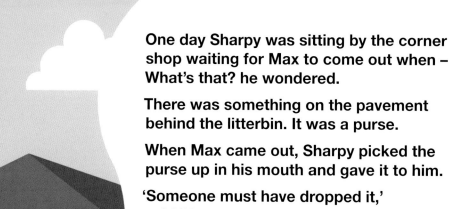

One day Sharpy was sitting by the corner shop waiting for Max to come out when – What's that? he wondered.

There was something on the pavement behind the litterbin. It was a purse.

When Max came out, Sharpy picked the purse up in his mouth and gave it to him.

'Someone must have dropped it,' said Max.

Max didn't look inside. He took it straight to the shopkeeper.

'Someone will be looking for this,' he said. 'Please give it back to them if they come here asking for it.'

 God wants us always to be honest in what we say and what we do.

Max took the lost purse to the shopkeeper. What else could you do if you found something someone has lost?

Pens Prayer

Please be with me every day, dear Jesus, and teach me what is right and what is wrong. Thank You. Amen.

Living like Jesus

'So let us not become tired of doing good ...'
(Galatians 6 v 9)

A friend in need

It was Pens' swimming day.
They were heading for the pool
when they saw Splodge sitting
by herself in her garden.

Hello, Splodge,
what are you
doing?

Nothing, Squiggle's
gone out and I'm all
on my own.

'Come to the pool with us,' invited Denzil.

Splodge shook her head. 'I can't swim,' she answered sadly.

'We could stay here and keep you company,' suggested Charlotte.

'What, and miss swimming?' frowned Max.

'We can go swimming tomorrow,' Charlotte replied, 'but Splodge needs a friend today.'

 Jesus never stopped being kind to people, even when they were unkind to Him.

Which of these six things can you do: swim, ride a bike, make your bed, write the letters of the alphabet, remember your telephone number, tie your shoelaces?

Pens Prayer

Lord Jesus, please help me to be kind and good and loving, even when I don't feel like it. Amen.

49

Day 24 — Living like Jesus

'… how happy are those who hear the word of God and obey it!' (Luke 11 v 28)

No picnic

Gloria and Marco were going on a picnic.

'I've forgotten juice,' Gloria said. 'Stay here while I go to the shop – and don't eat the food!'

But the food looked delicious, and Marco was getting hungrier and hungrier.

'I could just have one cake,' he said to himself, 'and perhaps a sandwich, and maybe some biscuits.'

Marco ate ... and ate ...

In the end, there was nothing left. And he felt a bit sick.

'You've spoilt the picnic!' cried Gloria, crossly. 'Not just for you; for me, too.'

Sometimes it was hard for Him, but Jesus always listened to His Father God and obeyed Him.

Do you have any favourite places for picnics?

Pens Prayer

Father God, when I don't feel like doing what You want me to do, may I remember everything You have done for me, and try again. Amen.

Day 25 — Living like Jesus

'Trust in the LORD with all your heart.' (Proverbs 3 v 5)

The dependable friend

Philippa had broken her glasses.

52

'Let's go to the optician and get some new ones,' smiled Charlotte.

'But now I can't see very well,' worried Philippa. 'I might bump into something, or trip over something, or fall down.'

'Silly!' laughed Charlotte. 'I won't let you bump or trip or fall. I'll stay right beside you and make sure you're safe.'

'Will you really?' asked Philippa.

'Definitely,' announced Charlotte. 'There's no need to worry. You can depend on me.'

 In the happy times and in the difficult times, Jesus trusted His Father God to be with Him.

Oh, no! What am I going to do?

Pens have learned lots of ways to live like Jesus. How many of them can you remember?

Pens Prayer

Thank You so much, Lord God, for sending Jesus to be our friend and to show us how to live for You. As I grow bigger, may I remember to follow Him day by day. Amen.

ONE KIND MAN
A Samaritan helps out

Day 26

'... do this and you will live.' (Luke 10 v 28)

Jesus tells a story

A man asked Jesus, 'What must I do to be friends with God forever?'

Jesus answered, 'Tell Me what you think you should do.'

'I should love God,' the man said, 'and I should love my neighbour as much as I love myself.'

'That's right,' replied Jesus.

'But who is my neighbour?' the man went on.

'Listen to this story,' Jesus smiled. 'It'll help you to understand.'

Jesus often used stories to teach people how to be close to God.

Who tells you stories?

Pens Prayer

Lord Jesus, please help me to live the way You want me to every day. Amen.

One Kind Man
A Samaritan helps out

Day 27

'… when he saw the man, he walked on by, on the other side.' (Luke 10 v 31)

Help!

'One day,' Jesus began, 'a man was walking from a place called Jerusalem to another place called Jericho, when some robbers jumped out at him. They hit him and they stole his money. Then they ran off and left him lying in the road.

'After a while, a priest from the Temple walked by. Did he stop when he saw the poor man? Did he run to help him? No.' Jesus shook His head. 'He just passed on by.'

 When someone needs us, we should try to help them.

 Can you think of any ways to be UN-selfish?

Pens Prayer

Dear God, it's so easy to be selfish. Help me to think about others more, and myself less. Amen.

One Kind Man
A Samaritan helps out

Day 28   '... his heart was filled with pity.' (Luke 10 v 33)

A friend at last

The people listening to Jesus' story wondered, 'Did anyone else find the poor man?'

'Yes,' Jesus went on. 'Another man from the Temple. He, too, crossed the road and walked by on the other side. But then along came a man from Samaria.'

'A Samaritan?' the people frowned. 'We don't like Samaritans.'

'I know,' said Jesus, 'but this Samaritan looked after the poor man. He cleaned his cuts and soothed his bruises.'

When we help someone, we are being kind like Jesus.

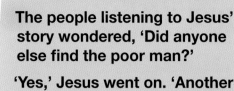

Are there times when your friends have been kind to you?

Pens Prayer

Thank You, Lord Jesus, that You never get tired of caring for us. Amen.

One Kind Man
A Samaritan helps out

Day 29

'Take care of him … and when I come back this way, I will pay you whatever else you spend on him.' (Luke 10 v 35)

Safe again

'What happened next?' the people wanted to know.

Jesus said, 'When the Samaritan had made the man more comfortable, he put him on his donkey. Then he took him to an inn to have a rest.

'"Stay here until you feel better," said the Samaritan to the poor man. "I'll give the innkeeper some money to look after you."'

 The Samaritan did everything he could to help.

When might someone need you to be a good friend?

Pens Prayer

Father God, may I always be happy to help someone who needs me. Amen.

One Kind Man
A Samaritan helps out

Day 30

'... which one of these three acted like a neighbour towards the man attacked by the robbers?' (Luke 10 v 36)

A **very good** neighbour

Jesus had finished telling His story. So He looked at the man who had asked Him, 'Who is my neighbour?'

'Three men saw the poor man who'd been hurt by robbers,' Jesus said. 'Which one of them behaved like a neighbour to him?'

'The one who helped him,' the man answered. 'The Samaritan man.'

'That's right,' smiled Jesus. 'People who help us, and people we help – they are all our neighbours. See who you can help today.'

Looking after each other makes God happy and brings us closer to Him.

How could you be kind to someone today?

Pens Prayer

I thank You, Lord Jesus, for being so gentle and so kind. Please help me to grow more like You every day. Amen.

Other Pens titles

Visit www.cwr.org.uk for list of National Distributors.

All scripture references are from the GNB: Good News Bible © 1996, 1971, 1976 American Bible Society.

Concept development, editing, design and production by CWR

Printed in China by 1010 Printing Ltd.

ISBN: 978-1-85345-555-1

OTHER CWR DAILY BIBLE-READING NOTES
Every Day with Jesus for adults
Inspiring Women Every Day for women
Lucas on Life Every Day for adults
Cover to Cover Every Day for adults
Mettle for 14- to 18-year-olds
YP's for 11- to 15-year-olds
Topz for 7- to 11-year-olds